WAIT FOR ME!

Duddles is late for lunch. Can you help him join the flock as they look for food?

Illustrated by Charles Jordan

Answer on page 47.

DISGUISE THE LIMIT

How good a detective are you? See if you can match each photograph with one of the suspects in disguise outside the window. Look for similar items that may give you a clue as to who's who.

WANTED
SLIP MAHONEY

WANTED
SATCH JONES

WANTED
ROCKY SULLIVAN

WANTED
YUKON SAM

WANTED
VIRGIL STARK

WANTED
MAE R. MAYNOTT

WANTED
DON GOINDERE

WANTED
MA GUMP

WANTED
DINAH SAUR

WANTED
SIEGFRIED

Illustrated by Marc Nadel

WHERE AM I?

Can you figure out where you are by using each of your five senses?

A. You see........a green diamond.
You hear ......crowd cheers.
You smell .....grass.
You feel ....a wooden seat.
You taste......a hot dog.

A baseballgame

B. You see ....a skeleton.
You hear......boo!
You smell.....a pumpkin.
You feel ....a mask on your face.
You taste .....candy.

Hallwe Hallaween

C. You see ....a booth with games.
You hear......a barker with a megaphone.
You smell ....ponies.
You feel ....a steel safety bar.
You taste .....cotton candy.

A fair

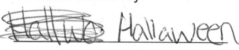

D. You see........a tent.
You hear ......birds.
You smell .....a fire.
You feel........a twig in your hand.
You taste......a roasted marshmallow.

A camp

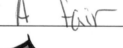

Illustrated by Jerry Zimmerman

Answer on page 47.

INSTANT PICTURE

Fill in every space that contains two dots
to find the fast way home.

Answer on page 47.

LOST WORDS

Each group of words below is missing one item. See if you can identify the lost word and put it in the right spot on the grid.

ACROSS

1. Pooh, Piglet, Tigger, Kanga, Roo, Rabbit, Eeyore, ___ ___ ___

2. ___ ___ ___ ___ ___ ___ ___ ___, Pennsylvania, New Jersey, Georgia, Connecticut, Massachusetts, Maryland, South Carolina, New Hampshire, Virginia, New York, North Carolina, Rhode Island

5. Red, orange, yellow, green, ___ ___ ___ ___

7. Guatemala, Belize, El Salvador, Honduras, Nicaragua, ___ ___ ___ ___ ___ ___ ___ ___, Panama

9. ___ ___ ___ ___ ___, Ontario, Michigan, Erie, Superior

10. Beth, Meg, Amy, ___ ___

11. Pinkie, ring, middle, index, ___ ___ ___ ___ ___

13. Africa, Antarctica, Asia, Australia, ___ ___ ___ ___ ___ ___, North America, South America

14. Fee, fi, ___ ___, fum

16. Mercury, Venus, Earth, Mars, Jupiter, Saturn, Uranus, ___ ___ ___ ___ ___ ___ ___, Pluto

17. ___ ___ ___ ___ ___, sticks, brick

19. Penny, nickel, ___ ___ ___ ___, quarter, half-dollar

22. ___ ___ ___ ___, Pinta, Santa Maria

23. Argentina, Bolivia, Brazil, Chile, Colombia, Ecuador, French Guiana, Guyana, Paraguay, ___ ___ ___ ___

24. Smell, touch, sight, hearing, ___ ___ ___ ___ ___

Illustrated by Rich Johnson

DOWN

1. July, August, September, ___ ___ ___ ___ ___ ___ ___

2. ___ ___, re, me, fa, so, la, ti

3. Scarecrow, Tin Woodman, Cowardly ___ ___ ___ ___

4. Aries, Taurus, Gemini, Cancer, ___ ___ ___

5. Sleepy, Doc, Dopey, Happy, Grumpy, Sneezy, ___ ___ ___ ___ ___ ___ ___

6. Catcher, pitcher, first base, second base, ___ ___ ___ ___ ___ ___ ___ ___, third base

7. Dasher, Dancer, Prancer, Vixen, Cupid, Donner, Blitzen, Rudolph, ___ ___ ___ ___ ___

8. Lincoln, Jefferson, Washington, ___ ___ ___ ___ ___ ___ ___

12. ___ ___ ___, Larry, Curly

14. Wednesday, Thursday, ___ ___ ___ ___ ___ ___

15. Johnson, Nixon, Ford, Carter, ___ ___ ___ ___ ___ ___

18. Water, earth, fire, ___ ___ ___

20. Solid, liquid, ___ ___ ___

21. Five, four, three, two, ___ ___ ___

SHELL SHOCK

Don't be shocked as you search for shells.
How many can you pick up in this scene?

Illustrated by Judith Hunt

WHERE NO MAN HAS GONE

Last month was very exciting—four new galaxies were discovered!
Each galaxy was found by a different scientist (one scientist is
Williams), and each scientist named the galaxy he found and its
central star (or sun). From the information provided, can you
determine which galaxy each scientist found and the name of that
galaxy's central star?

Use this chart to keep track of your answers. Put an "X" in boxes
that can't be true and an "O" in boxes where the information
matches. For example, clue 2 says Williams named his sun Luna. Put
an "O" in the box where the Williams row meets the Luna column.
Put "X"s in the rest of that row and the three other boxes of that
column.

		Galaxy				Central Star/Sun			
		Adriatic	Baltic	Celtic	Damask	Luna	Mega	Niko	Osa
Scientist	Williams					O	X	X	X
	Xeno					X			
	Yukon					X			
	Zeke					X			

1. The four new galaxies are: the one discovered by Yukon;
   the one whose sun has been named Niko; the galaxy
   discovered by Xeno; and Celtic.
2. Williams named the sun Luna in the galaxy he found (which
   is neither Adriatic nor Damask).
3. Osa is the central star of the galaxy Baltic.
4. Xeno discovered the galaxy whose central star is Mega,
   while Zeke discovered the Adriatic galaxy.

FUN FINGERS

This code features the manual or hand alphabet used primarily by deaf people to fingerspell words. See if you can use the alphabet below to decode the limerick on the next page.

Illustrated by Judith Hunt

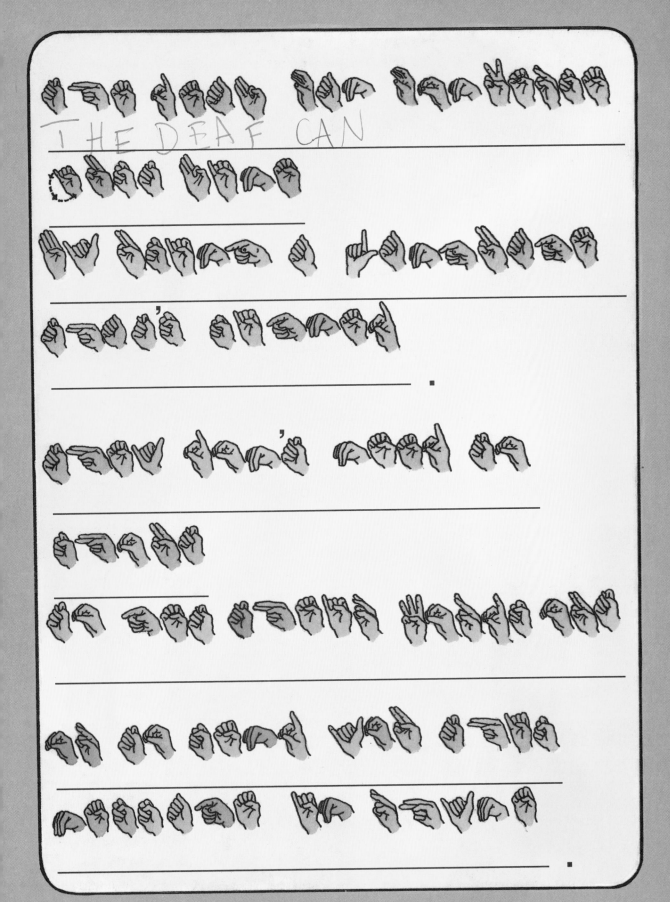

THE DEAF CAN

PICTURE MIXER

Copy these mixed-up squares in the spaces on the next page to put this picture back together. The letters and numbers tell you where each square belongs. The first one, A-2, has been done for you.

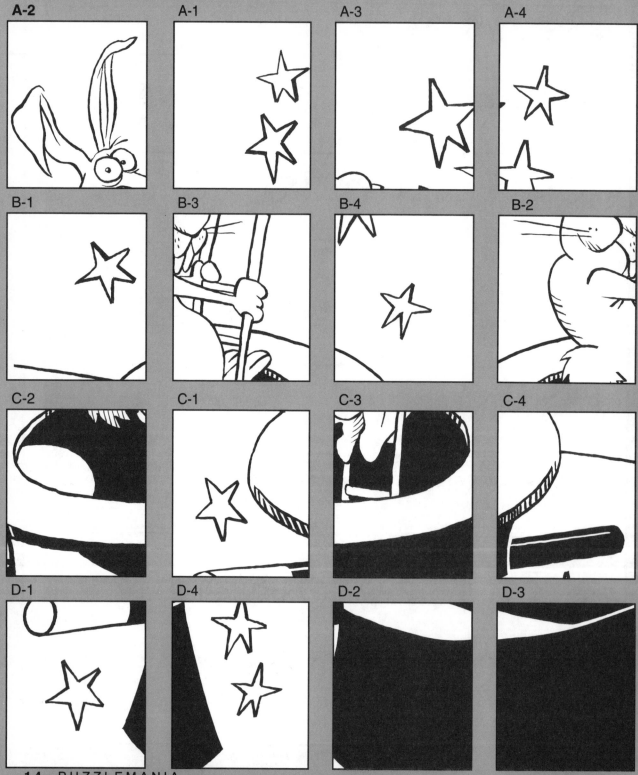

Illustrated by Jeff Stahler

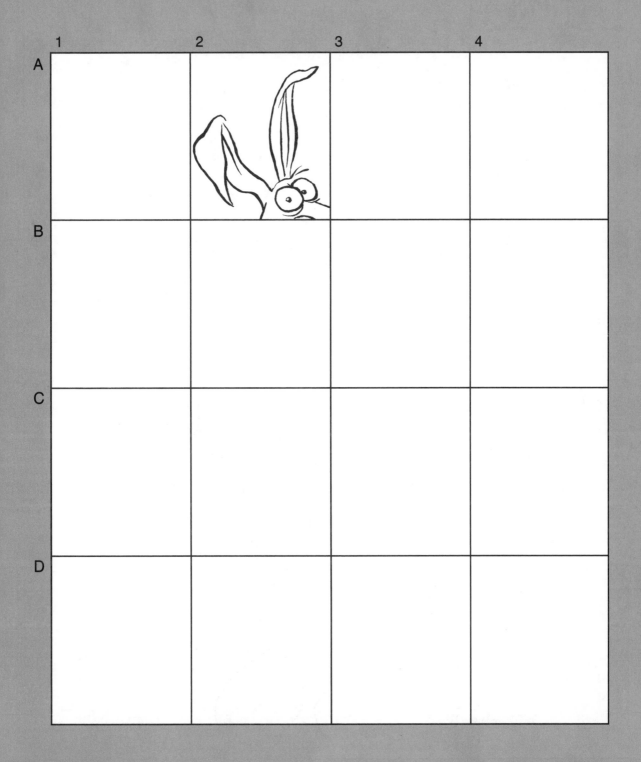

	1	2	3	4
A				
B				
C				
D				

DINO DIFFERENCES

How many differences can you see between the pictures below?

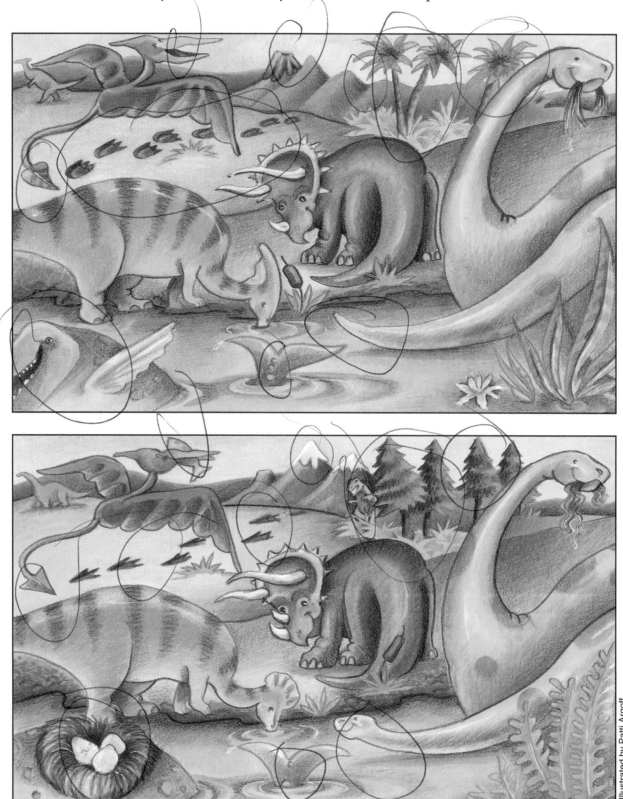

Illustrated by Patti Argoff

SCRAMBLED SHARKS

Many sharks share their names with common objects or other animals. Using the pictures as clues, unscramble the letters below each line to name twelve such sharks.

D E R H M A H M A E

U L B L

G R I T E

O L N E M

E R E E L S P

R O H N

W A S

T A G E R   T H I W E

H E L A W

S U N E R

N A L E G

D L A R O P E

Illustrated by Anni Matsick

Answer on page 48.

THE RED SEE

Roses are red, hearts are, too. This is the only puzzle where ketchup is... blue? First, find all the things that are usually red in this picture. Then find the words for these pictures and circle them in the grid. Look across, backward, up, down, and diagonally.
We found 17 things in all.

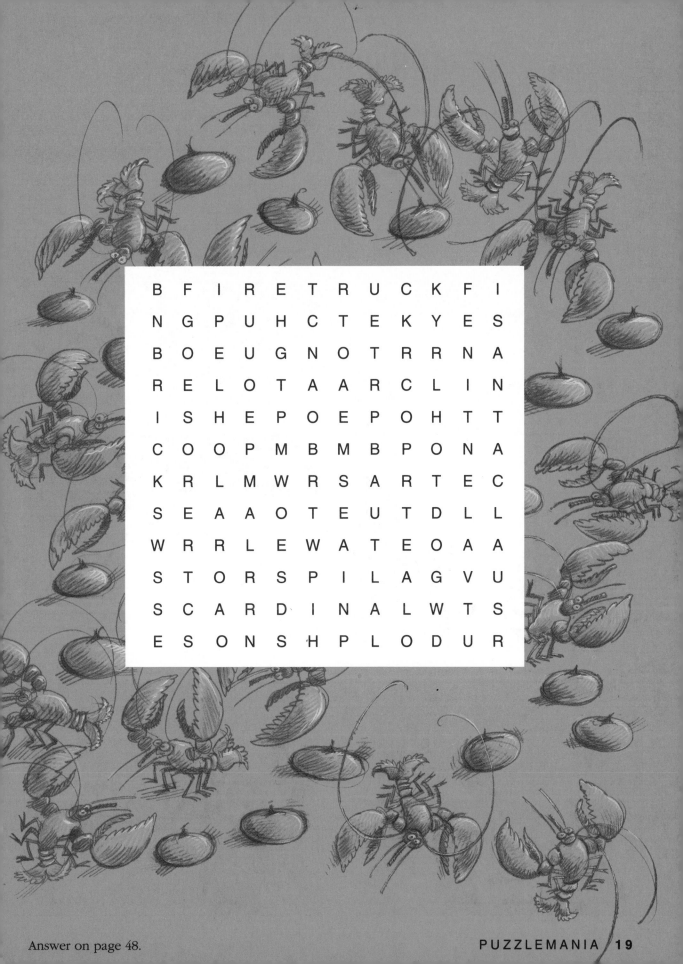

B F I R E T R U C K F I
N G P U H C T E K Y E S
B O E U G N O T R R N A
R E L O T A A R C L I N
I S H E P O E P O H T T
C O O P M B M B P O N A
K R L M W R S A R T E C
S E A A O T E U T D L L
W R R L E W A T E O A A
S T O R S P I L A G V U
S C A R D I N A L W T S
E S O N S H P L O D U R

WHAT HAPPENED WHEN?

Can you number these historical scenes to show
which happened first, second, and so on?

Illustrated by Judith Hunt

Answer on page 48.

STOP, LOOK, AND LIST

Under each category, list four things that begin with the letter "T." For example, one number that begins with "T" is Thirty. See if you can name a few more.

NUMBERS

1

2

3

4

BODY PARTS

Been

Skull

Shoulder

Spine

BOY'S NAMES

Ben

coal

James

Jordan

Illustrated by Lisa Dayer

MUSICAL INSTRUMENTS

Flute

carraret

trumpet

harp

Answer on page 48.

HIDDEN PICTURES

There are at least 23 objects hidden in this scene.
How many can you find?

CAN YOU RECALL?

The Excel Electrical Company has just issued a recall on several of its appliances. The employees at Apple's Appliances are now trying to figure out which products are affected by the recall. Can you help them find out which appliances they should return?

RADIO
Model No. I369
Serial No. 6075

VCR
Model No. K322
Serial No. 6144

REFRIGERATOR
Model No. I263
Serial No. 5678

CLOCK
Model No. P539
Serial No. 7654

FREEZER
Model No. G166
Serial No. 6538

MICROWAVE
Model No. B49
Serial No. 1234

DISHWASHER
Model No. E1573
Serial No. 6852

TELEVISION
Model No. J452
Serial No. 4004

Illustrated by Charles Jordan

RECALL SPECIFICATIONS:

1. If the model number starts with a vowel and the serial number ends in an even number, then the product is NOT being recalled.

2. If the model number starts with a consonant and the serial number starts with an odd number, then the product IS being recalled.

3. If the model number and serial number both end in even numbers, then the product is NOT being recalled.

4. If the sum of the digits in the model number is the same as the sum of the digits in the serial number, then the product IS being recalled.

Answer on page 48.

DOT MAGIC

Connect these dots to discover something
you should have on hand for emergencies.

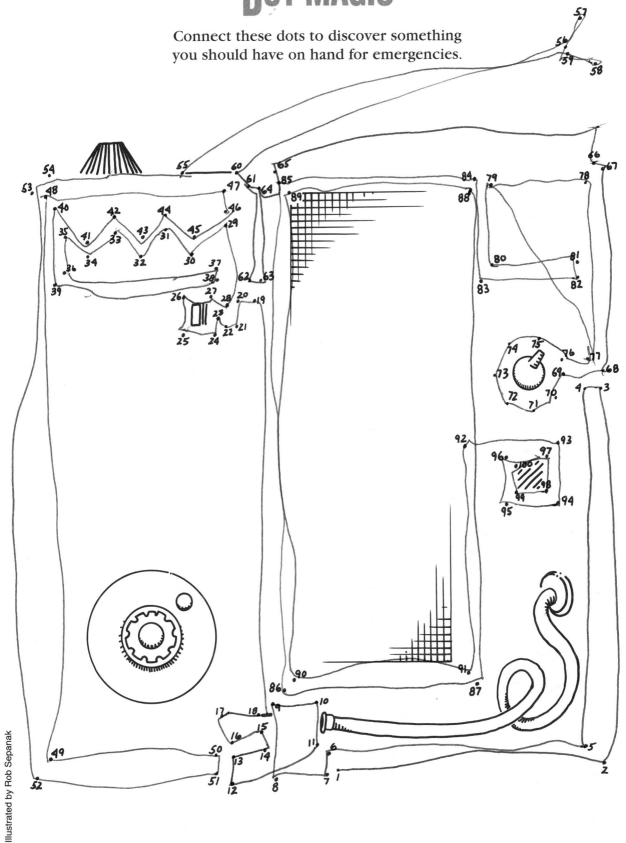

Answer on page 48.

THE CASE OF THE UNHAPPY GOOSE

Read the story and fill in the missing words. Then match the numbered letters with the corresponding spaces at the end of the story. If you've filled in the spaces correctly, you'll help Greg solve this problem.

Greg Gosling was having a terrible day. When he got ___ ___ ___ ___ from school, all
         9   6

he wanted to do was cry.

"What's ___ ___ ___ ___ ___ , darling?" asked Greg's mother.
        10 8   3   15 2

"This was the worst day of my life. I didn't do well on my math test. My

homework blew away. Harry Hippopotamus sat on my lunch. And the Bulldog

Bullies made fun of me on the way home."

"Well, I'm sorry about your day." Greg's mom gave him a big hug. "You'll do

better on the next test if you study harder. And next time, be sure to put

your homework someplace secure."

"Yes, Mom," Greg said.

"And I'm sure Harry didn't mean to sit on your lunch. But now tell me about

those ___ ___ ___ ___ ___ ___ ___ ___ ."
       12 4   7   5

"They made fun of me almost the whole ___ ___ ___ home!" Greg sniffed back a tear.
<small>14   1</small>

"What did they say?"

"They said I was just a silly goose who would never grow up."

Greg's mom smiled. "Well, I don't think you're silly, but they were half

right. You never will grow up."

"Oh, Mom! Not you, too."

"Don't worry, honey. You'll get older, but you won't grow up."

"What do you mean?"

"The next time ___ ___ ___ ___ ___ bullies make fun of you,
<small>13   11</small>

tell them a secret about something you can do that they can't. You tell them..."

Greg's mom whispered a secret in his ear that made him smile.

What was the secret?

___ ___ ___ ___ ___ ___
1   2   3   4   5   6

___ ___ ___ ___ ___ ___ ___ ___ ___ !
7   8   9   10   11   12   13   14   15

SHOPPER STOPPER

You might think twice before shopping at Sam's Shoe Store.
How many unusual things can you see in this picture?

SAM'S SHOE SAIL

Illustrated by Kit Wray

KIDS' SNEEKERS 3 FOR $10.

$15 OFF! ALL LADIES TENIS SHOES REG. $14.99

OPEN 12 HOURS ON SATERDAYS

HOURS
M-F 10 AM-6PM
SAT 9 AM-7PM
CLOSED
SUNDAY

EXIT

OUT

MEN'S BOOOTS 25% OFF!

Answer on page 49.

ORCHESTRA MEMORIES

Take a long look at this picture. Try to remember everything you see in it. Then turn the page and try to answer some questions about it without looking back.

DON'T READ THIS UNTIL YOU HAVE LOOKED AT "Orchestra Memories—Part I" ON PAGE 29.

ORCHESTRA MEMORIES   Part II

Can you answer these questions about the orchestra scene you just saw? Don't peek!

1. What was coming out of the saxophone?
2. How many candles were lit on the piano?
3. What did the sign on the piano say?
4. How many animals were in the scene?
5. What instrument was being played by the chef?
6. How many piano players were in the scene?
7. What color hat was the harmonica player wearing?
8. Who was wearing thimbles?

Answer on page 49.

STATE THE FACTS

Each of these four-letter words is made up of two elements. Can you state what they are?

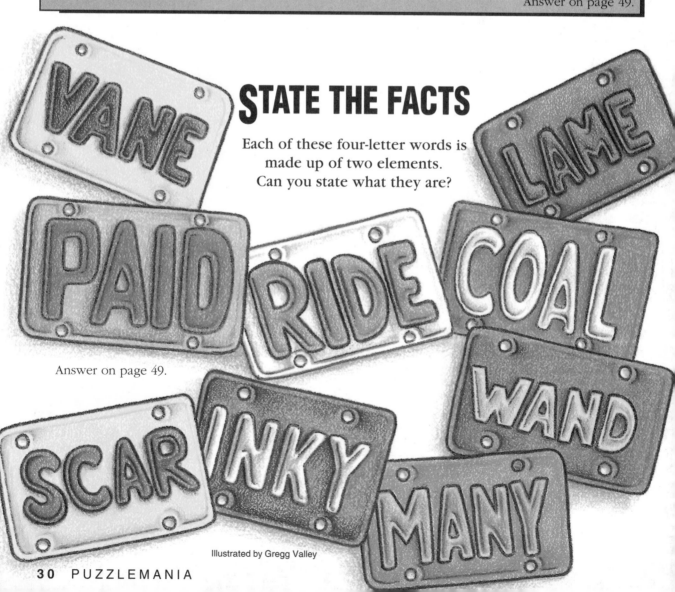

Answer on page 49.

Illustrated by Gregg Valley

UNDER LOCK AND KEY

Lock in on the answers by keying in on the clues. Each of the missing words has either LOCK or KEY in its answer. Can you find the missing words?

1. This holds a picture and is worn on a chain around the neck: L O C K ___ ___

2. A stubborn animal with long ears: ___ ___ ___ K E Y

3. The Three Bears found her in their house: ___ ___ ___ ___ ___ L O C K ___

4. This animal can hang from a tree by its tail: ___ ___ ___ K E Y

5. This person makes keys: L O C K ___ ___ ___ ___

6. The black-and-white part of the piano: K E Y ___ ___ ___ ___ ___

7. Another name for tetanus: L O C K ___ ___ ___

8. This bird is a favorite at Thanksgiving: ___ ___ ___ K E Y

9. Instrument that tells time: ___ L O C K

10. Central stone of an arch: K E Y ___ ___ ___ ___

GLOBE PROBE

That famous explorer Dr. Cincinnati Holmes is looking on his map for the names of some of his friends. Each friend lives in a country whose name contains his or her name. For instance, his friend Tina can be found in Argentina. Can you find at least one country for each of these names? The names appear in order and aren't scrambled.

ADA _____

AL _____

ANA _____

ARI _____

BEN _____

CHAD _____

DOMINIC _____

DON _____

FRAN _____

GARY _____

GERI _____

GUY _____

Greenland

Alaska (U.S.)

Canada

United States

Hawaii (U.S.)

Cuba

Belize

Dominican Republic

Mexico

Venezuel

Trinidad

El Salvador

Guyana

Nicaragua   Panama

Colombia

Ecuador

Peru

Brazil

Bolivia

Paraguay

Chile

Argentina

Uruguay

IRA _____   MARK _____

KEN _____   PHILIP _____

LEON _____   SAL _____

LIZ _____   STAN _____

MAL _____   TRINI _____

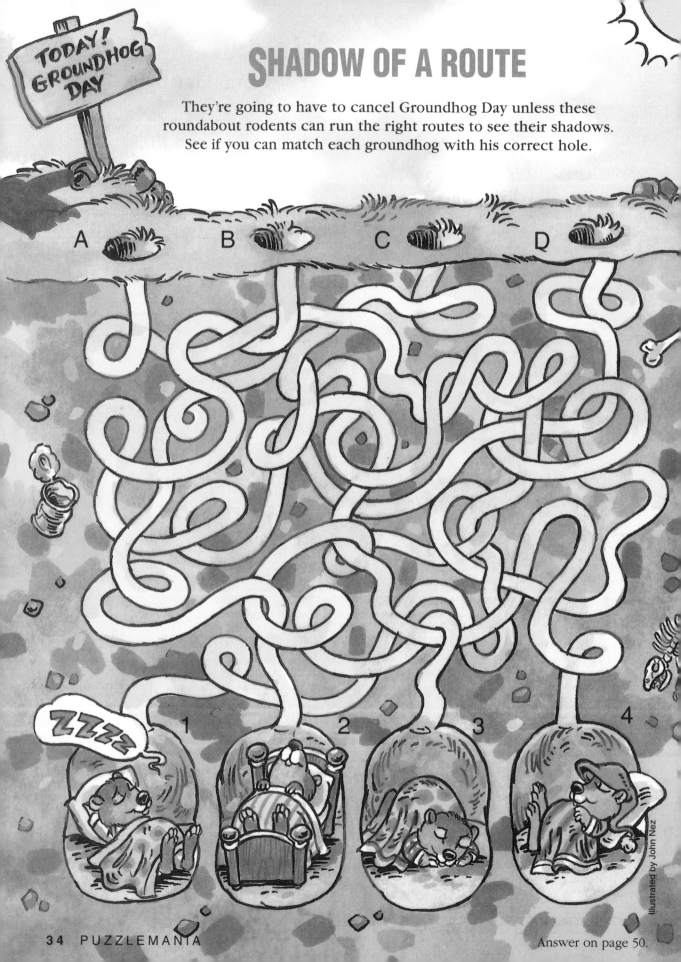

SHADOW OF A ROUTE

They're going to have to cancel Groundhog Day unless these roundabout rodents can run the right routes to see their shadows. See if you can match each groundhog with his correct hole.

TODAY! GROUNDHOG DAY

A   B   C   D

1   2   3   4

Answer on page 50.

Illustrated by John Nez

SUB WAYS

To find your way through this maze, subtract the first pair of numbers (10-8). Draw a line to the answer (2), then move directly ahead to the next pair of numbers and do the same. Answers may be to the left, right, up, or down, but the next problem will always be straight ahead.

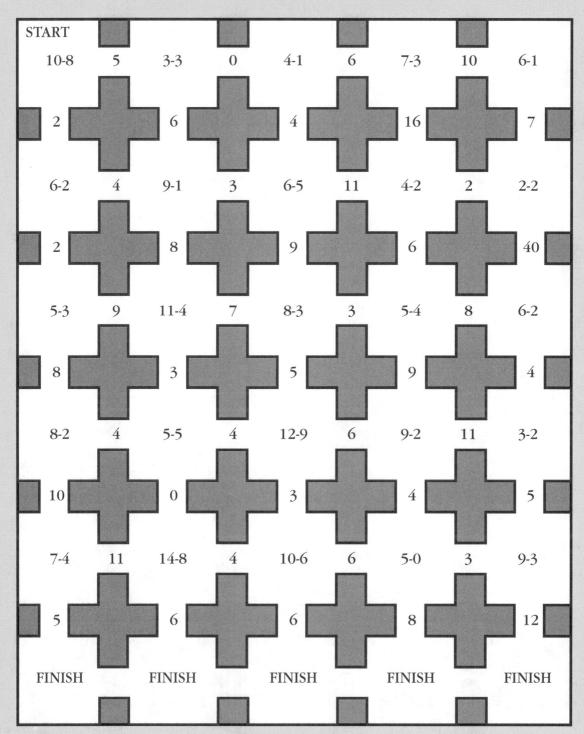

START

| 10-8 | 5 | 3-3 | 0 | 4-1 | 6 | 7-3 | 10 | 6-1 |

| 2 | | 6 | | 4 | | 16 | | 7 |

| 6-2 | 4 | 9-1 | 3 | 6-5 | 11 | 4-2 | 2 | 2-2 |

| 2 | | 8 | | 9 | | 6 | | 40 |

| 5-3 | 9 | 11-4 | 7 | 8-3 | 3 | 5-4 | 8 | 6-2 |

| 8 | | 3 | | 5 | | 9 | | 4 |

| 8-2 | 4 | 5-5 | 4 | 12-9 | 6 | 9-2 | 11 | 3-2 |

| 10 | | 0 | | 3 | | 4 | | 5 |

| 7-4 | 11 | 14-8 | 4 | 10-6 | 6 | 5-0 | 3 | 9-3 |

| 5 | | 6 | | 6 | | 8 | | 12 |

FINISH   FINISH   FINISH   FINISH   FINISH

Answer on page 50.

AWESOME OFFICES

Follow the clues below to discover the answer to our riddle.
Put each letter you find in the right spot, placing the same
letters on spaces with similar numbers.

There is a plant in the window below the first letter.
Watch out for pigeons when you grab the third letter.
An air-conditioner is holding up letter number twelve.
Letter six is in the lower left-hand corner.
A cat is sleeping next to letter eleven.
Letter number four is directly below letter eleven.
Number two has an antenna wire running to the roof.
There are purple curtains in the window with letter eight.
Letter nine is in the window with the fish tank.
Don't disturb the spider web as you pull off letter seven.
The fan is blowing in the room behind letter ten.
Letter five is the third from the top on the word running
down the side of the building.
The thirteenth letter is in an office that's for rent.

Why do writers like to work in office buildings?

___ ___ ___ ___ ___ ___ ___ ___ ___ ___ ___ ___ ___ ___
1   2   3   4   5   6   2   7   8   2   9   2   4   9   2

___ ___ ___ ___ ___ ___ ___ ___ ___ ___ ___ ___ ___ .
4   10 11 7   11 12   6   7   11 9   13 2   6

Answer on page 50.

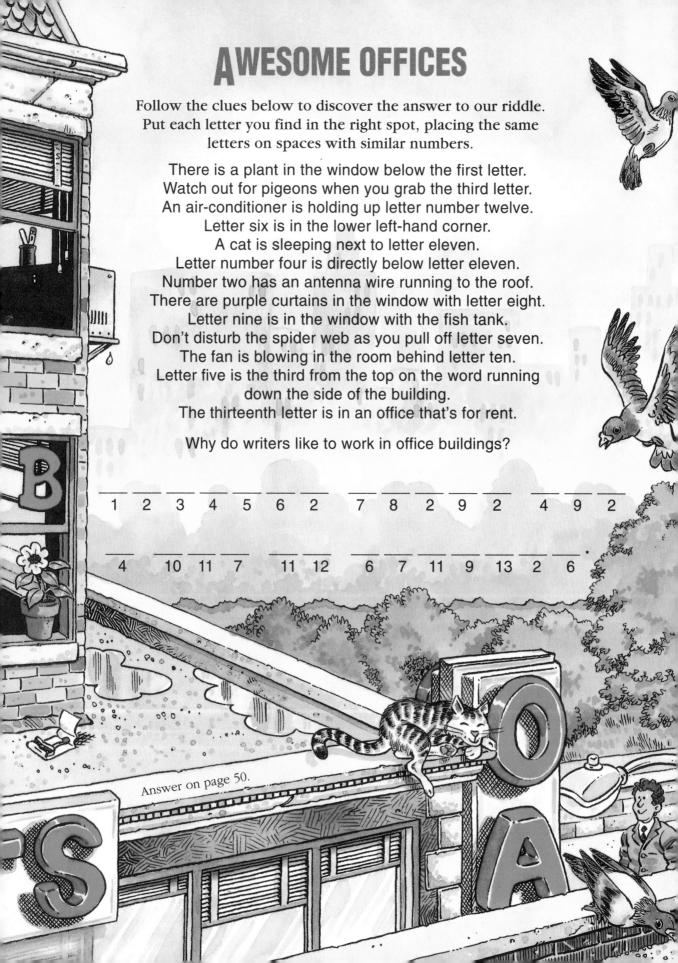

ROW, ROW, ROW

Each of these beach buildings has something in common
with the sand sculptures in the same row. For example,
all the scenes in the top row across have a shovel in
them. Look at the other rows across, down, and
diagonally. What's the same about each row of three?

Illustrated by Anni Matsick

Answer on page 50

DON'T LOOK NOW

What's that in the sideview mirror? Is it a police officer on a pogo stick or a swan on a skateboard? Use your imagination to draw in what you think is right behind you.

ANIMALS DOWN UNDER

All of these animals and birds are native wonders from the land down under, Australia. Can you fit all their names into the grid on the next page? Use the number of letters in each word as a clue to find where it goes.

3 LETTERS
bat
emu

5 LETTERS
dingo
koala

6 LETTERS
lizard
parrot
wombat

7 LETTERS
opossum
tuatara

8 LETTERS
anteater
cockatoo
kangaroo
lyrebird
parakeet
platypus

9 LETTERS
bandicoot
black swan
bowerbird
cassowary

10 LETTERS
kookaburra

Illustrated by Marc Nadel

Answer on page 50.

WHAT'S NEXT?

Can you guess what figure comes next in each row?

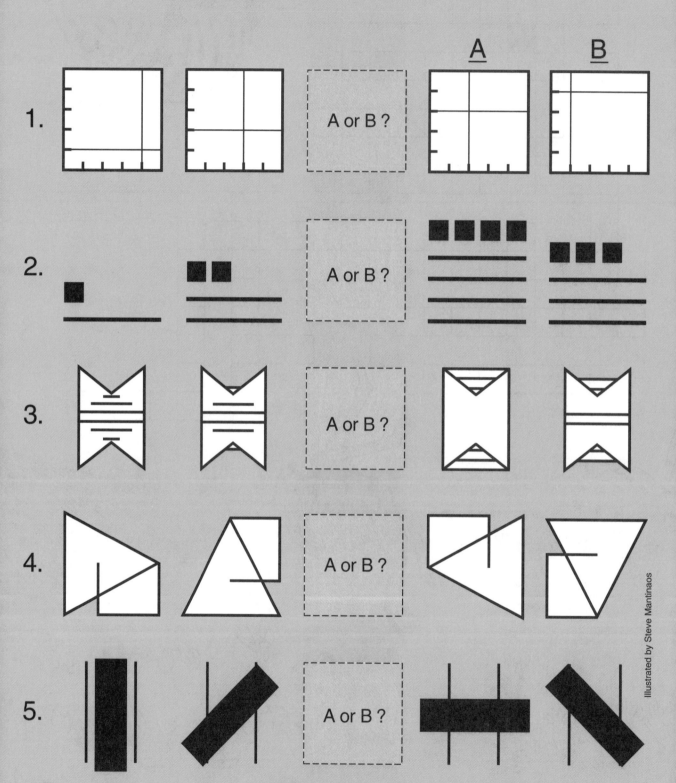

Illustrated by Steve Mantinaos

Answer on page 50.

WHAT'S IN A WORD?

We turned on the lights to look for all the words hidden in the letters of CHANDELIER. We found a lot of words that have three letters or more in them. You must be very bright if you can shed light on 100 words or more.

Illustrated by Teresa Howell

WHO THOUGHT OF THAT?

One of the greatest inventors in history lived almost 500 years ago. He is famous for creating more than 100 inventions, gadgets, and fantastic ideas that were later developed more fully by other inventors. Some of his inventions are pictured here. Fill in the blanks with the name of each invention. When you have filled in all the blanks, the circled letters will spell out the name of this mystery inventor.

1.

2.

3.

4.

5.

6.

8.

9.

7.

10.

11.

12.

13.

Illustrated by Terry Rogers

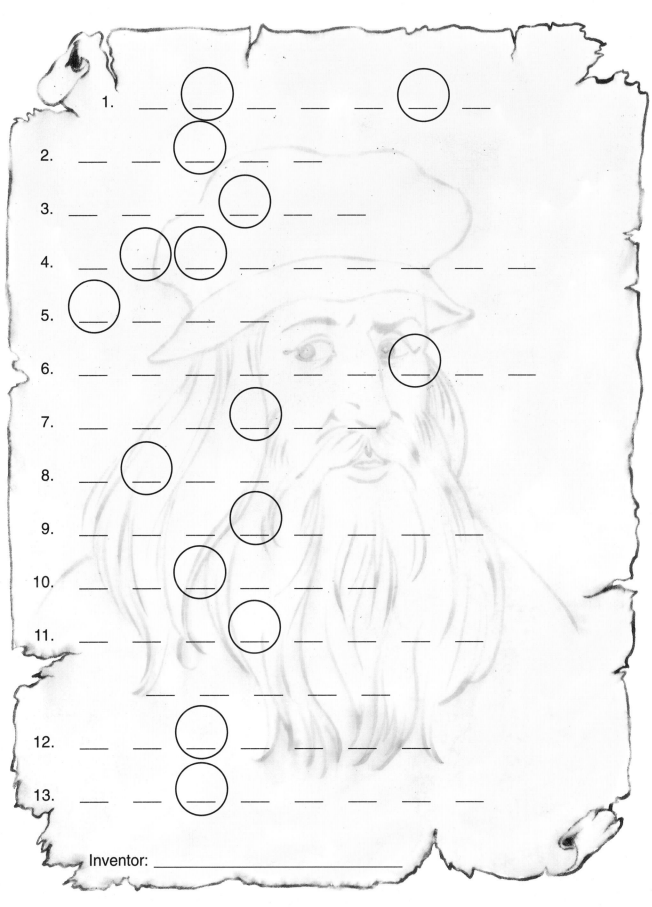

1. ___ ___ ___ ___ ___ ___ ___ ___ ___

2. ___ ___ ___ ___ ___

3. ___ ___ ___ ___ ___ ___ ___

4. ___ ___ ___ ___ ___ ___ ___ ___ ___

5. ___ ___ ___ ___

6. ___ ___ ___ ___ ___ ___ ___

7. ___ ___ ___

8. ___ ___ ___

9. ___ ___ ___ ___ ___ ___ ___

10. ___ ___ ___ ___ ___

11. ___ ___ ___

___ ___ ___ ___ ___

12. ___ ___ ___ ___ ___ ___ ___

13. ___ ___ ___ ___ ___ ___ ___

Inventor: _____

MATCHING A-TIRE

See if you can match each wheel with its corresponding vehicle.

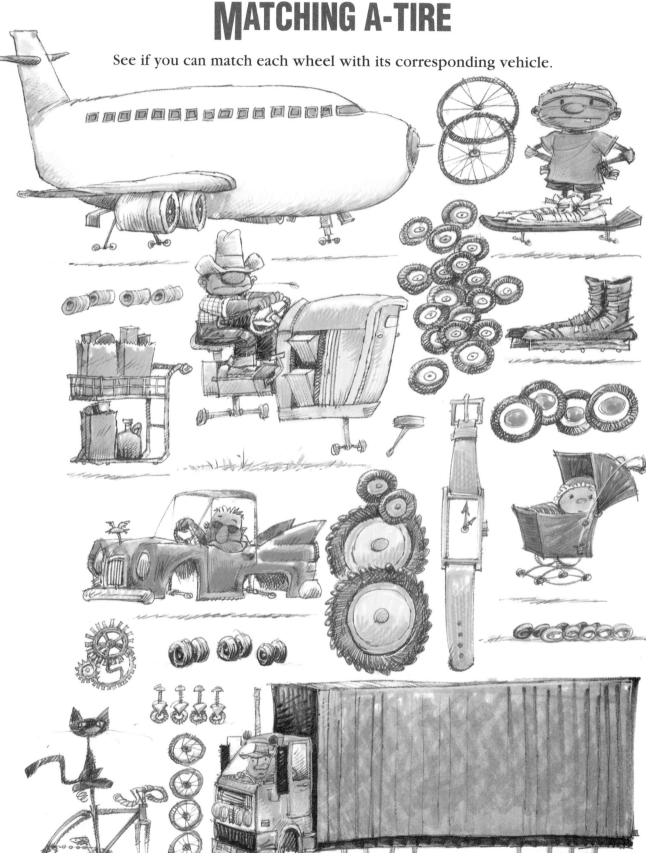

Answer on page 50.

ANSWERS

WAIT FOR ME! (page 3)

DISGUISE THE LIMIT (pages 4-5)

WHERE AM I? (page 6)

A - baseball game   C - carnival

B - Halloween party   D - campsite

INSTANT PICTURE (page 7)

LOST WORDS (pages 8-9)

¹O	W	L		²D	³E	L	A	W	A	R	E		⁴L
C				O	I					⁵B	L	U	E
T		⁶S		⁷C	O	S	T	⁸A		R	I	C	A
O		⁹H	U	R	O	N		S					O
B		O		M			¹⁰J	O		¹¹T	H	¹²U	M	B
¹³E	U	R	O	P	E		¹⁴F	O	S			F	O		¹⁵R
R		T		E			R		¹⁶N	E	P	T	U	N	E
		S					I			U			L		A
	¹⁷S	T	¹⁸R	A	W		¹⁹D	I	M	E		²⁰G		²¹O	G
		O	I				A			L		A		²²N	Ñ	A
	²³P	E	R	U			Y		²⁴T	A	S	T	E		N

WHERE NO MAN HAS GONE (page 11)

The sun of Williams's galaxy is Luna (clue 2). Williams did not discover the galaxy of Adriatic (clue 2), Damask (clue 2), or Baltic (clue 3); he discovered the Celtic galaxy.

The galaxy with the sun Niko was not found by Yukon or Xeno (clue 1); it was discovered by Zeke. Therefore, Zeke must have discovered the Adriatic galaxy (clue 4).

Xeno discovered the galaxy whose central star is named Mega (clue 4). By elimination, Yukon discovered the galaxy whose central star is Osa. Yukon's galaxy is Baltic (clue 3). Therefore, Xeno's galaxy is Damask.

In summary, the answer is:
Williams, Celtic, Luna
Xeno, Damask, Mega
Yukon, Baltic, Osa
Zeke, Adriatic, Niko

		Galaxy				Central Star/Sun			
		Adriatic	Baltic	Celtic	Damask	Luna	Mega	Niko	Osa
Scientist	Williams	X	X	O	X	O	X	X	X
	Xeno	X	X	X	O	X	O	X	X
	Yukon	X	O	X	X	X	X	X	O
	Zeke	O	X	X	X	X	X	O	X

FUN FINGERS (pages 12-13)
The deaf can converse just fine
By using a language that's signed.
They don't need to shout
To get their words out
Or to send you this message in rhyme.

PICTURE MIXER (pages 14-15)

SCRAMBLED SHARKS (page 17)
Hammerhead
Bull
Tiger
Lemon
Sleeper
Horn
Saw
Great White
Whale
Nurse
Angel
Leopard

THE RED SEE (pages 18-19)

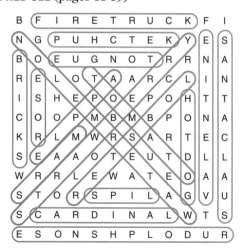

WHAT HAPPENED WHEN? (page 20)

5	3
4	6
2	1

STOP, LOOK, AND LIST (page 21)
Here are our answers. You may have found others:

Numbers:
Ten
Three
Twelve
Two

Body Parts:
Thumb
Toe
Tongue
Torso

Boys' Names:
Tim
Todd
Tom
Tony

Musical Instruments:
Trombone
Trumpet
Tuba
Tympani

CAN YOU RECALL? (page 24)
The microwave, radio, and clock are being recalled.

DOT MAGIC (Page 25)

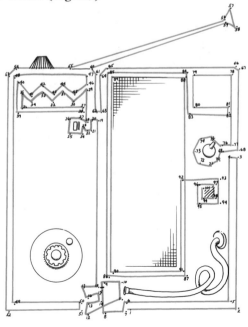

THE CASE OF THE UNHAPPY GOOSE (pages 26-27)

Greg Gosling was having a terrible day. When he got HOME from school, all he wanted to do was cry.

"What's WRONG, darling?" asked Greg's mother.

"This was the worst day of my life. I didn't do well on my math test. My homework blew away. Harry Hippopotamus sat on my lunch. And the Bulldog Bullies made fun of me on the way home."

"Well, I'm sorry about your day." Greg's mom gave him a big hug. "You'll do better on the next test if you study harder. And next time, be sure to put your homework someplace secure."

"Yes, Mom," Greg said.

"And I'm sure Harry didn't mean to sit on your lunch. But now tell me about those BULLDOGS."

"They made fun of me almost the whole WAY home!" Greg sniffed back a tear.

"What did they say?"

"They said I was just a silly goose who would never grow up."

Greg's mom smiled. "Well, I don't think you're silly, but they were half right. You never will grow up."

"Oh, Mom! Not you, too."

"Don't worry, honey. You'll get older, but you won't grow up."

"What do you mean?"

"The next time THOSE bullies make fun of you, tell them a secret about something you can do that they can't. You tell them..."

Greg's mom whispered a secret in his ear that made him smile.
What was the secret?
A GOOSE GROWS DOWN!

SHOPPER STOPPER (page 28)

Here are just 10 of the unusual things we found. There are still others.

1. SAIL should be SALE.
2. Neither door is for entering.
3. Three and nine are switched on the clock.
4. SNEEKERS should be SNEAKERS.
5. Sneakers are sold in pairs, not groups of three.
6. TENIS should be TENNIS.
7. Ladies' shoes are incorrectly priced—you can't take $15 off a price of $14.99.
8. BOOOTS should be BOOTS.
9. SATERDAYS should be SATURDAYS.
10. The store is only open ten hours on Saturdays.

ORCHESTRA MEMORIES (page 30)

1. Bubbles
2. Two
3. Out To Lunch
4. Two—a monkey and a cat
5. Triangle
6. None
7. Green
8. The washboard player

STATE THE FACTS (page 30)

Each word is made up of a pair of abbreviations for the names of two of the fifty states.

PAID (Pennsylavania and Idaho)
SCAR (South Carolina and Arkansas)
VANE (Virginia and Nebraska)
RIDE (Rhode Island and Delaware)
INKY (Indiana and Kentucky)
LAME (Louisiana and Maine)
COAL (Colorado and Alabama)
WAND (Washington and North Dakota)
MANY (Massachusetts and New York)

UNDER LOCK AND KEY (page 31)

1. LOCKET
2. DONKEY
3. GOLDILOCKS
4. MONKEY
5. LOCKSMITH
6. KEYBOARD
7. LOCKJAW
8. TURKEY
9. CLOCK
10. KEYSTONE

GLOBE PROBE (pages 32-33)

Here are our answers. You may have found others.

ADA	Canada
AL	Italy
ANA	Botswana
ARI	Bulgaria
BEN	Benin
CHAD	Chad
DOMINIC	Dominican Republic
DON	Indonesia
FRAN	France
GARY	Hungary
GERI	Algeria
GUY	Guyana
IRA	Iran
KEN	Kenya
LEON	Sierra Leone
LIZ	Belize
MAL	Mali
MARK	Denmark
PHILIP	Philippines
SAL	El Salvador
STAN	Afghanistan
TRINI	Trinidad

SHADOW OF A ROUTE (page 34)
A–3, B–4, C–1, D–2

SUB WAYS (page 35)

AWESOME OFFICES (pages 36-37)
Why do writers like to work in office buildings? Because there are a lot of stories.

ROW, ROW, ROW (page 38)

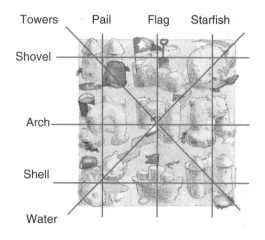

ANIMALS DOWN UNDER (pages 40-41)

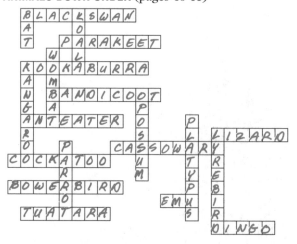

WHAT'S NEXT? (page 42)
1. A   2. B   3. B   4. A   5. A

WHAT'S IN A WORD? (page 43)
We were able to shed light on 135 words. You may have found others.

ace, ache, acid, ade, aid, ail, air, alder, and, arc, arch, are, cad, can, candle, cane, car, card, care, chain, chair, chandler, char, cheer, chide, child, children, chin, cider, clad, clean, clear, cradle, crane, cried, dale, dance, dare, deal, dean, dear, decline, deer, deli, den, denial, dial, dice, die, din, dine, diner, dire, drench, each, ear, eel, elder, end, endear, era, hail, hair, hale, hand, handle, hard, harden, hare, heal, hear, heard, heed, heel, held, herd, hide, hind, hinder, hire, ice, ideal, idle, inch, ire, lace, lad, laden, laid, lain, lair, lance, lancer, land, lane, lard, lead, lean, led, leech, leer, lend, liar, lice, lichen, lid, lie, lied, lien, line, nadir, nail, near, need, nice, race, raid, rail, rain, ranch, reach, read, real, recline, red, reed, reel, rein, relied, rend, rice, rich, rid, ride, rile

WHO THOUGHT OF THAT? (pages 44-45)
1. Glasses
2. Clock
3. Wrench
4. Parachute
5. Drum
6. Telescope
7. Glider
8. Tank
9. Elevator
10. Pliers
11. Spinning wheel
12. Bicycle
13. Flippers

MYSTERY INVENTOR: LEONARDO DA VINCI

MATCHING A-TIRE (Page 46)